PAUL JENKINS

ANDY CLARKE

REPLICA

VOLUME
1

THE TRANSFER

DAN BROWN

MARCELO MAIOLO

CLAYTON COWLES

AFTERSHOCK

LICA

VOLUME 1

THE TRANSFER

PAUL JENKINS creator & writer

ANDY CLARKE artist

MARCELO MAIOLO (#1) & **DAN BROWN** (#2-5) colorists

CLAYTON COWLES letterer

ANDY CLARKE w/ **MARCELO MAIOLO** front cover

ANDY CLARKE w/ **MARCELO MAIOLO** (#1-2) &
        DAN BROWN (#3-5) original covers

ANDREW ROBINSON & **PHIL HESTER** variant covers

JOHN J. HILL book & logo designer

MIKE MARTS editor

AFTERSHOCK

MIKE MARTS - Editor-in-Chief • **JOE PRUETT** - Publisher • **LEE KRAMER** - President
JAWAD QURESHI - SVP, Investor Relations • **JON KRAMER** - Chief Executive Officer
MIKE ZAGARI - SVP Digital/Creative • **JAY BEHLING** - CFO • **MICHAEL RICHTER** - Chief Creative Officer
STEPHAN NILSON - Publishing Operations Coordinator • **LISA Y. WU** - Social Media Coordinator

AfterShock Trade Dress and Interior Design by **JOHN J. HILL**
AfterShock Logo Design by **COMICRAFT**
Proofreading by **DOCTOR Z.**
Publicity: contact **AARON MARION** (aaron@fifteenminutes.com) &
RYAN CROY (ryan@fifteenminutes.com) at **15 MINUTES**

AFTERSHOCKCOMICS.COM   Follow us on social media 🐦 📷 f

INTRODUCTION

BY **PAUL JENKINS**

In case you're wondering, Trevor Churchill is me, Paul Jenkins.

These days I'm a novelist, a studio head, a director and writer of animation, a videogame creator, a comic book writer, a teacher and who-knows-what else. Not a day goes by that I don't wish I could clone myself fifty times.

The problem is, I'm pretty sure the clones and I would not get along. Because I'm kind of an asshole. I have bad habits, like always needing to be the driver of a car (can't be a passenger since I broke my neck). I play golf far too quickly and I sneeze a lot. Can you imagine fifty of that idiot? Believe me, one is more than enough.

But, you know, I'd like to think that's why Trevor is such an endearing character. We all have a little bit of Trevor in us – trying to do the right thing and never succeeding, barely suffering the fools around us, and never taking no for an answer. Truth be told, I actually like the guy after having written him for a while.

Now, to business: I did so much less of the work than the rest of the creative team, and so this is a great place to shout them out, or whatever it is you kids do these days. Thanks to Andy Clarke, without whom Vorgas and Veet would not be nearly as hilarious. I'm always amazed when I can give an artist certain humorous parameters and find they accomplished far more than my words ever could. Andy, you are a bloody little genius. Thanks also to Dan Brown and Clayton Cowles for their amazing work – you guys are true professionals, and deserve all the recognition you can get. This book is yours, too.

And thanks to Joe and Mike and all the AfterShock team, all of whom need about fifty clones of themselves. I know they appear to be an obvious money laundering front for the Chinese Mafia, but I'm getting more and more convinced these guys are legit and I am contractually obliged to say so.

Thanks for picking up our book. I know you will love it. And if you don't, you only have yourself to blame.

Which would be a lot easier if there were fifty of you.

Paul Jenkins
Atlanta, 2016

1

"BY THE BOOK"

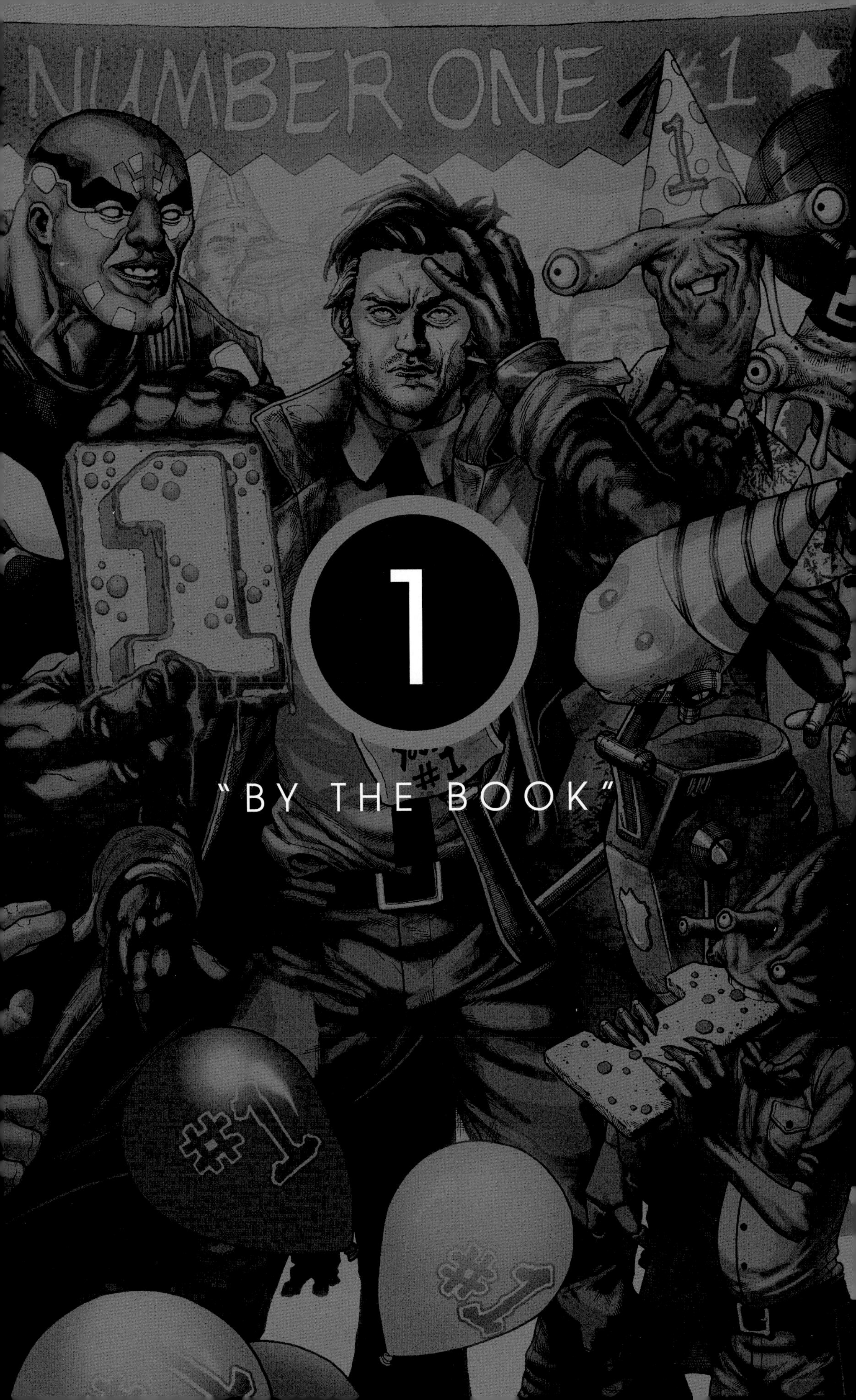

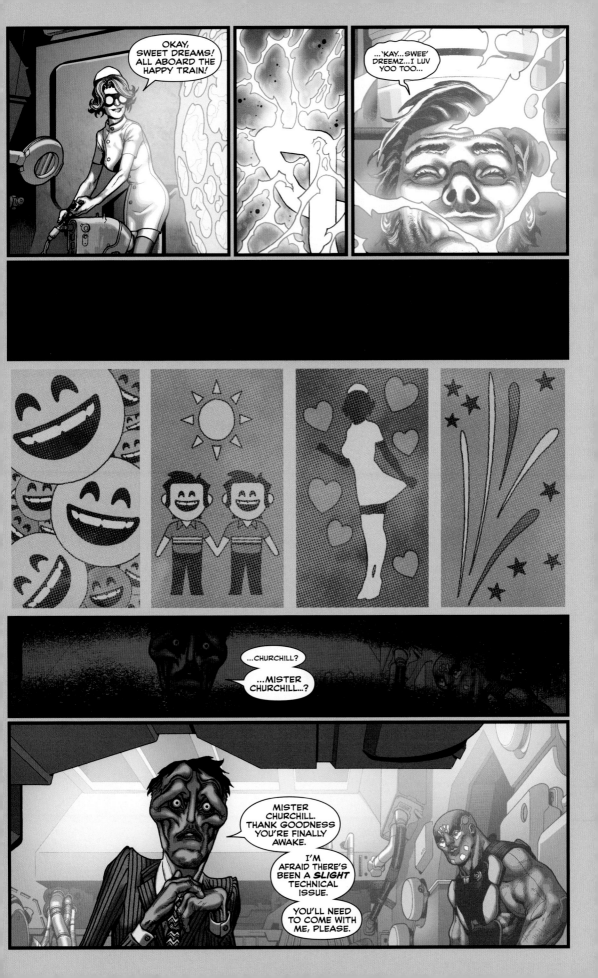

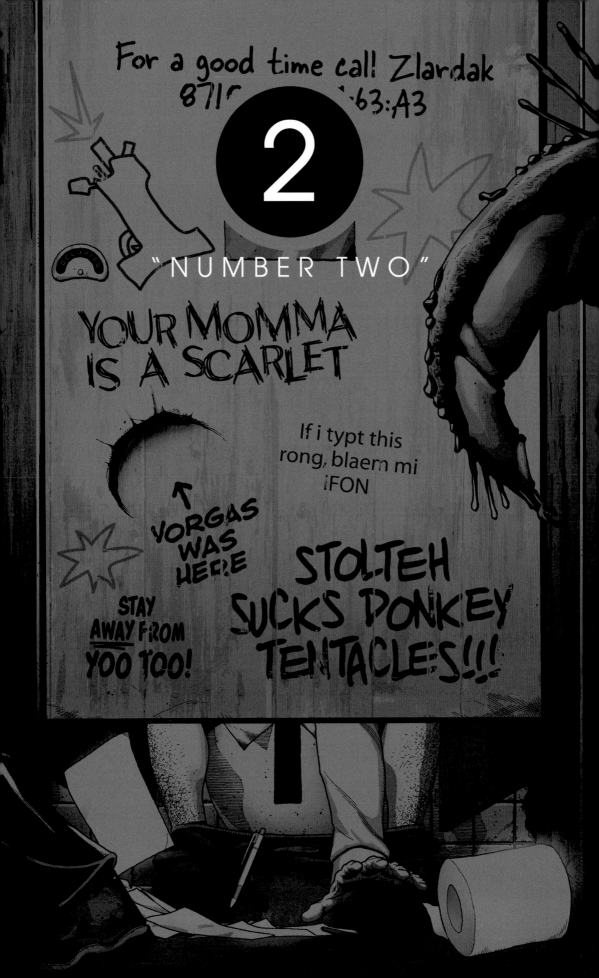

THIS IS NUMBER *TWO*. HIS HOBBIES INCLUDE PAPERWORK, MORE PAPERWORK, AND ACCIDENTALLY DROPPING ALL OF HIS PAPERWORK AT INOPPORTUNE MOMENTS.

HE HAS ASKED THAT WE REFER TO HIM BY NAME AS "*ROGER*." WE CALL HIM NUMBER TWO.

NUMBER TWO IS A CLONE: THE SECOND VERSION OF *ME*. I WASN'T FEELING VERY CREATIVE AT THE TIME HE CAME INTO BEING, HENCE THE NAME, "*NUMBER TWO*."

THOUGH "*NUMBER TWO*" IS PRETTY APROPOS, CONSIDERING THE AMOUNT OF SHIT THIS GUY TAKES ON OUR BEHALF

IF THERE ARE PAPERS TO BE FILED, TWO'S OUR MAN. IF AN ANGRY SLUHRVVIAN WARRIOR SHOWS UP AT THE PRECINCT DEMANDING BLOOD, NUMBER TWO IS GOING TO BE VOLUNTEERED FOR DIPLOMAT DUTY.

WHATEVER THE PROBLEM, NUMBER TWO IS USUALLY THE ONE TO SOLVE IT.

LIKE *THIS* PROBLEM, FOR EXAMPLE.

THIS IS A NUMBER TWO OF EPIC PROPORTIONS.

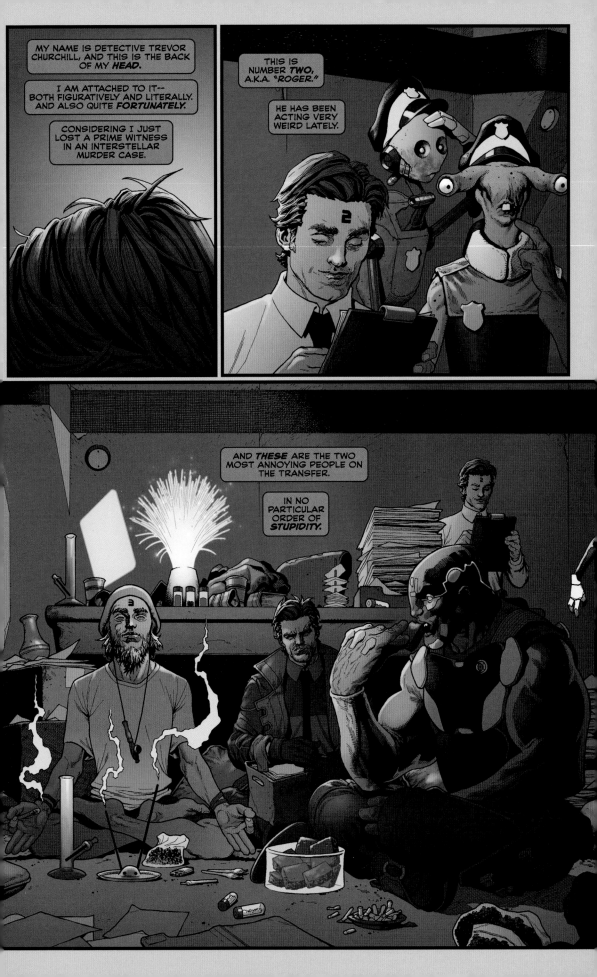

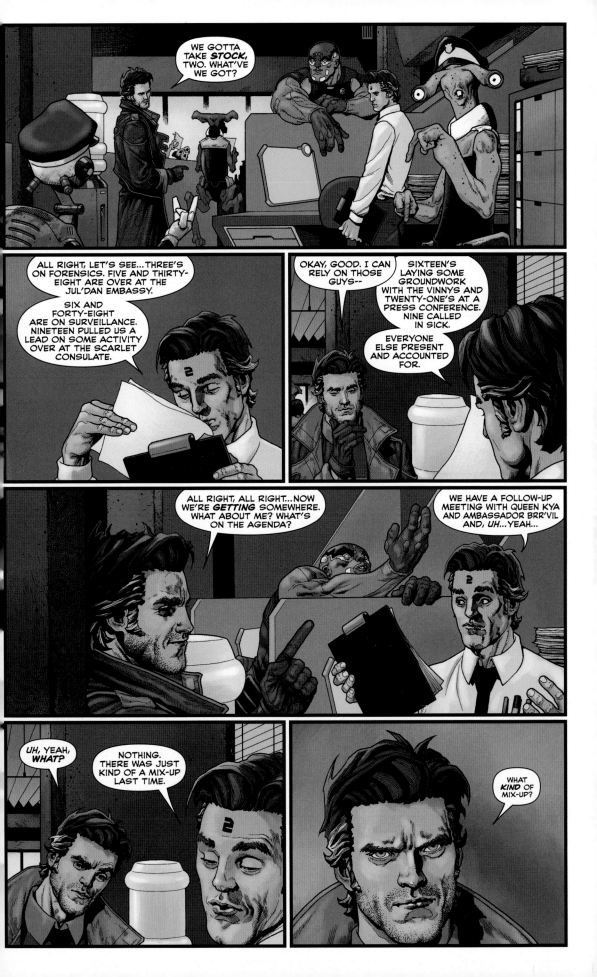

YOU DID *WHAT?*

IT WASN'T MY FAULT! I DIDN'T KNOW WHAT TO DO!

OH, SO YOU FIGURED IN LIEU OF A *SOLUTION* YOU'D CONSENT TO THE HORIZONTAL MAMBA WITH THE QUEEN OF AN ENTIRE *PLANET?*

SHORTNESS IS HIGHLY PRIZED IN THEIR CULTURE! I DIDN'T WANT TO OFFEND HER!

I'D SAY IT'S A BIT TOO *LATE* FOR THAT!

...OUR SOURCES CONFIRM THAT THE K'TARIAN EMISSARY'S MURDER IS LINKED TO SCARLET ACTIVITY IN THE QUADRANT.

SO FAR, WE HAVE BEEN UNABLE TO ASCERTAIN ANY REASON WHY THE JUL'DAN WOULD BE CONCERNED ENOUGH TO CLAIM RESPONSIBILITY.

AS YOU ARE NO DOUBT AWARE, INTERSTELLAR POLITICS IS UNRIVALED IN ITS COMPLEXITY. THERE ARE A NUMBER OF POSSIBLE FACTORS AT PLAY...

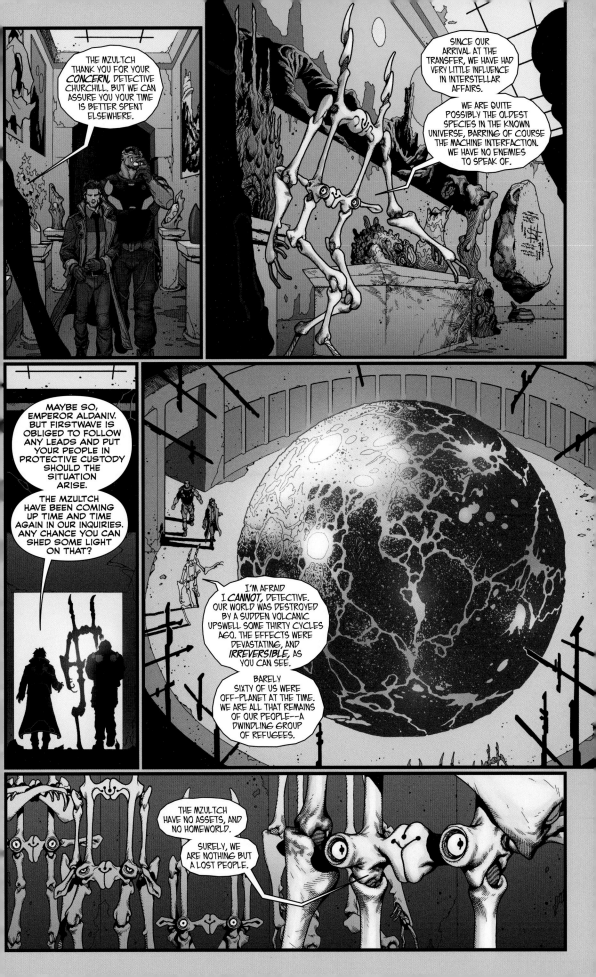

K'TARIAN EMBASSY.
RIGHT NOW.

ʕᑊᑎ⅃ᗅL ᒪ·ᑋᗅᑌᗱᗅИ

YOU SPEAK K'TARIAN, DETECTIVE. AND YOU PERFORM THE RITUAL OF GREETING AS IF YOU WERE ONE OF US. TELL ME, WHERE DID YOU LEARN OF SUCH THINGS?

IT NEVER HURTS TO KNOW WHO YOU'RE TALKING TO, EMISSARY.

INDEED. I WISH YOUR FELLOW DETECTIVE CHURCHILL HAD THE SAME INSIGHTS.

HE'S A GOOD MAN, EMISSARY. I WOULDN'T BE HERE WITHOUT HIM.

PERHAPS. NOW WHAT CAN I DO FOR YOU, CLONE NUMBER FOUR?

I WANTED TO SPEAK WITH YOU ABOUT THE SCARLET, SIR--

ᑌᑎⅭᒪᑋⅢᗅᗞᐢⅠ

SO IT IS TRUE--THE HEART OF A WARRIOR SPEAKS ALWAYS THE TRUTH. YOUR HATRED FOR THE SCARLET RUNS DEEP.

MAY YOUR AXE BE SATED BY THE BLOOD OF A THOUSAND OF THEIR NUMBER.

FIVE ALIVE!

"FIVE NAUGHTY MONKEYS"

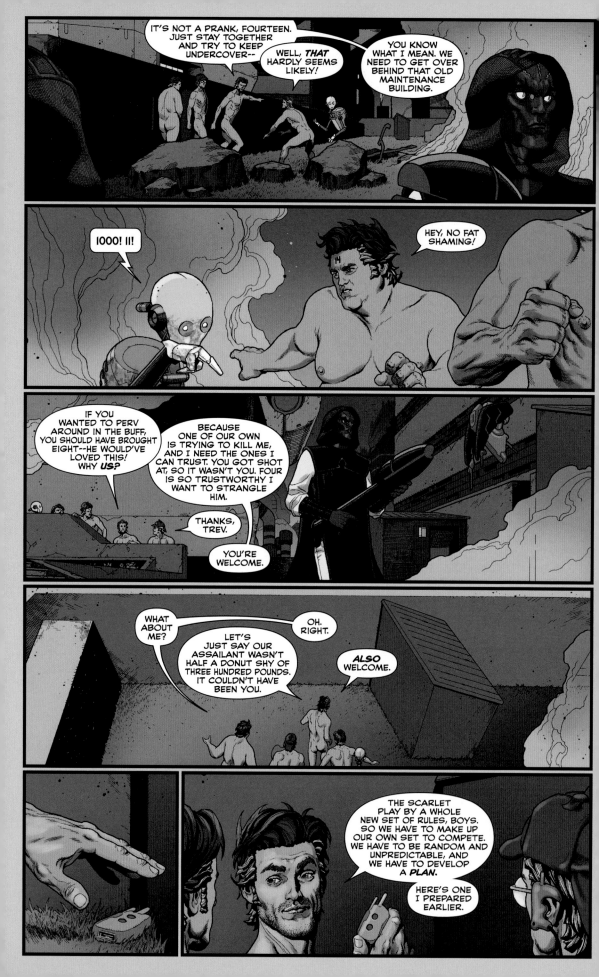

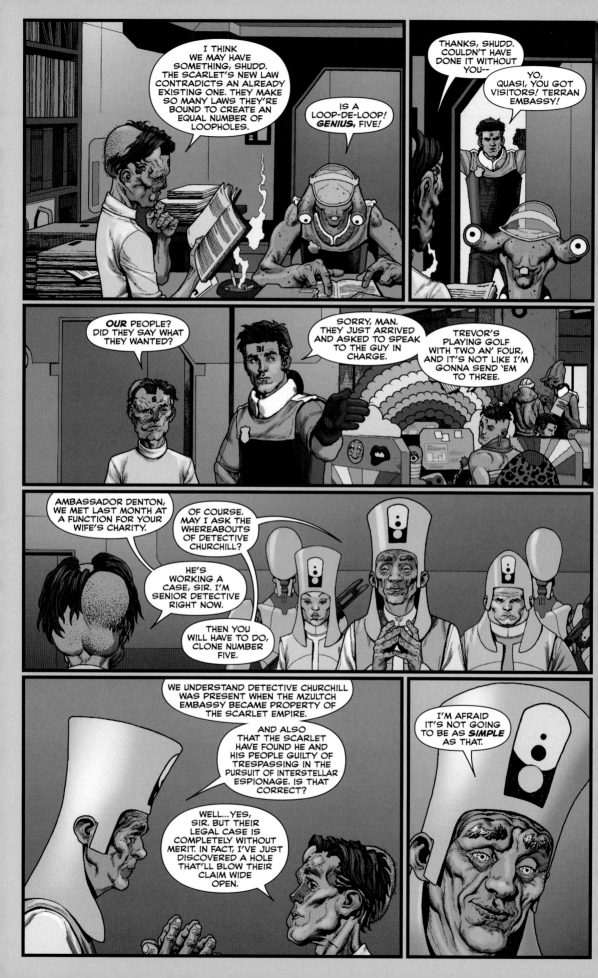

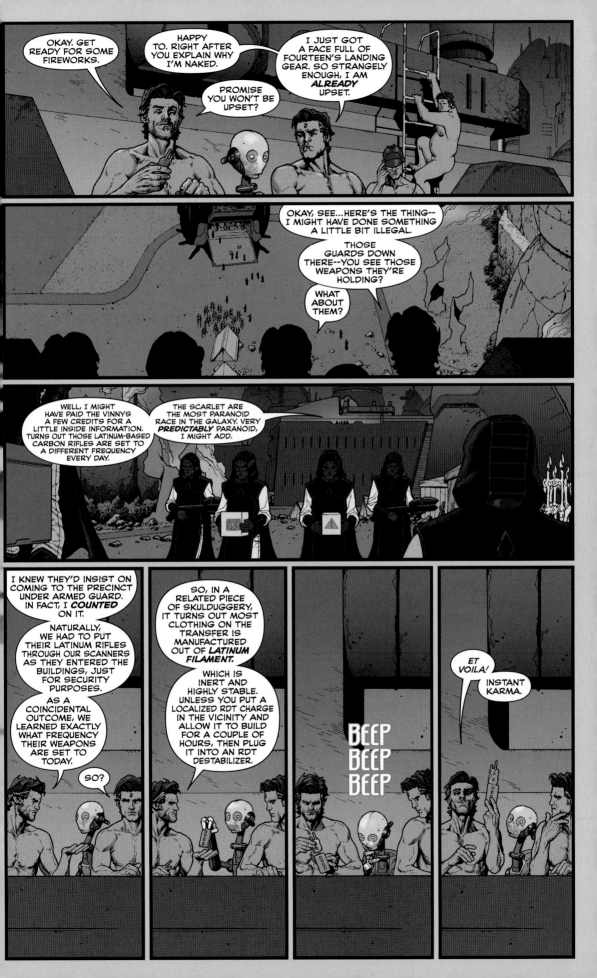

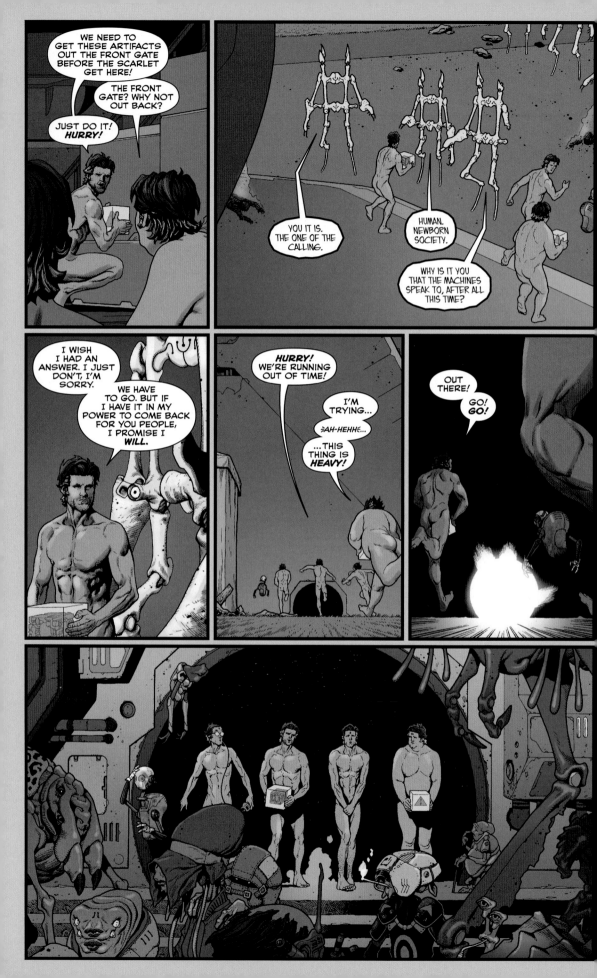

FIN.

issue 1
variant cover
ANDREW ROBINSON

One day, for no damn reason, the Animals woke up.
They started thinking. They started talking.
They started taking revenge.

ANIM(0)SITY

A NEW SERIES FROM
MARGUERITE BENNETT (INSEXTS)
AND **RAFAEL DE LATORRE** (SUPERZERO)

RESERVE THIS AFTERSHOCK SERIES TODAY!

AFTERSHOCK

PAUL JENKINS writer
🐦 @mypauljenkins

Paul Jenkins has been creating, writing and building franchises for over twenty years in the graphic novel, film and video game industries. Over the last two decades, Paul has been instrumental in the creation and implementation of literally hundreds of world-renowned, recognizable entertainment icons.

From his employment with the creators of the *Teenage Mutant Ninja Turtles* at the age of 22, to his preeminent status as an IP creator, Paul has provided entertainment to the world through hundreds of print publications, films, video games and new media. With six Platinum-selling video games, a Number One MTV Music Video, an Eisner Award, five Wizard Fan Awards, and multiple Best-Selling Graphic Novels, Paul Jenkins is synonymous with success. He has enjoyed recognition on the New York Times bestseller list, has been nominated for two BAFTA Awards and has been the recipient of a government-sponsored Prism Award for his contributions in storytelling and characterization.

Paul's extensive list of comic book credits include *Batman* and *Hellblazer* for DC Comics; *Inhumans, Spider-Man, The Incredible Hulk, Wolverine: Origin, Civil War: Frontlines, Captain America: Theater of War* and *The Sentry* for Marvel Comics; and *Spawn* for Image Comics.

ANDY CLARKE artist

Andy began working in comics in 1998 with writer Dan Abnett on *Sinister Dexter* for 2000AD. He made modest contributions to *Judge Dredd* (including a newspaper strip), worked on *Nikolai Dante* and *Shimura* with Robbie Morrison and with Kek-W on *Rose O'Rion*. He co-created *Thirteen* with Mike Carey and teamed up with Andy Diggle for *Snow/Tiger*. Since 2005, he has been very fortunate to work with some of the best writers on a small number of titles in the US: *Aquaman, R.E.B.E.L.S.* and *Batman* for DC and a *Mystique/Logan Legacy* one-shot for Marvel. He's also done the odd cover here and there.

MARCELO MAIOLO colorist
🐦 @MMaiolo

Marcelo Maiolo is best known for his work at DC Comics on such titles as *I, Vampire, Green Arrow, Demon Knights, Constantine, Green Lantern Corps, Teen Titans* and most recently, *Batman Beyond*. His work for other publishers includes *True Blood* for IDW, *King* for Jet City Comics, *Pacific Rim* for Legendary and *All-New X-Men* and *Old Man Logan* for Marvel. He lives and works in Brazil.

DAN BROWN colorist
🐦 @danbrowncomics

Hailing from the frozen prairies of central Canada, Dan Brown has been a colorist for every major publisher for the past 23 years. Dan is thrilled to be working with Mike Marts (who gave him his first coloring gig at Marvel, lo those many moons ago) and the rest of the fantastic AfterShock team to bring the next level in comic book entertainment!

CLAYTON COWLES letterer
🐦 @ClaytonCowles

Clayton Cowles graduated from the Joe Kubert School in 2009 and has been lettering full-time ever since. In addition to lettering for Marvel Comics, he works on the acclaimed Image titles *Bitch Planet, Phonogram, Pretty Deadly,* and *The Wicked + The Divine.* He lives in upstate New York with his cat.